Little red hen
and other stories

Nelson

Little red hen

A little red hen lived in a house
in a wood.
Near by lived a fox.
The fox wanted to catch
the little red hen and eat her up.
But the little red hen
shut her door every day.

One day the little red hen went out
to get some water.
The fox ran into the house and
hid behind the door.
The little red hen came back.
She did not see the fox.
She went into her house and
shut the door.

"Now I can catch you," said the fox.
He jumped onto the little red hen
and put her in a big sack.
"I am going to eat you
for my dinner," said the fox.

The fox took the sack and
went out of the house.
"Don't forget to cook me
with some carrots,"
said the little red hen.
So the fox put the sack down and
went to look for some carrots.

Then the little red hen cut a hole
in the sack. Snip. Snap. Snip.
She got out of the sack and
she put a big stone inside.
She tied up the sack and
she ran back home.

The fox came back.

He took the sack to his house.

He put a big pot of water
on the fire.

He threw the carrots into the pot
and he opened up the sack.

But instead of the little red hen,
all he saw was a big stone.
The fox was very cross.
So he did not have little red hen
for dinner after all.

The giant in the bed

A long time ago there was
a good giant.
He lived with his clever wife and
their little baby giant in
a house on a hill.

One day a big bad giant came along.
"Come out and fight," he said,
"or I will come and get you."
"What shall I do?" said the
good giant to his clever wife.

"Put on this bonnet," she said,
"and get into the baby's bed."
Just then there was a **bang** and
the bad giant opened the door.
"My giant is not here,"
said the clever wife.

"What a big baby you have,"
said the bad giant.
"Yes," said the clever wife.
"He is just like his Dad."

The clever wife had some buns.
She had some rocks that looked
just like the buns.
She gave a bun to the baby in
the bed and she gave a rock
to the bad giant.

The bad giant bit the rock.

He hurt his teeth.

He looked at the baby.

The baby ate the bun up.

"That baby must have strong teeth,"
said the bad giant.

"Yes, he has," said the clever wife.
"Put your finger in his mouth and
feel his strong teeth."
So the bad giant put his finger
in the baby's mouth and
the baby bit it hard.

"Ow, ow," said the bad giant.
"If that is your baby,
I don't want to fight his Dad."
He ran out of the house and
the good giant and his clever wife
never saw the bad giant again.

Henny Penny

One day Henny Penny was
in the garden when **bonk**,
something hit her on the head.
"Dear me," said Henny Penny.
"The sky is falling.
I must go and tell the king."

Off she went down the road and
she met Cocky Locky.
"Where are you going?"
said Cocky Locky.
"I am going to tell the king
that the sky is falling,"
said Henny Penny.
"A piece of it fell on my head."

"Can I come too?" said Cocky Locky.
So they set off down the road.
Then they met Ducky Lucky,
Goosey Loosey and Turkey Lurkey.
"Where are you going?" they asked.

"We are going to tell the king
that the sky is falling,"
said Henny Penny and Cocky Locky.
"A piece of it fell on my head,"
said Henny Penny.
"Can we come too?" said Ducky Lucky,
Goosey Loosey and Turkey Lurkey.

So they all went down the road,
past a farm and past a house
and over a bridge.
Then they met Foxy Woxy.
"Where are you going?"
said Foxy Woxy.
"We are going to tell the king that
the sky is falling," they all said.

"Come this way," said Foxy Woxy.
"This is a short cut."
Soon they came to a dark hole.
This was Foxy Woxy's den but
he did not tell them so.

"Follow me," said Foxy Woxy.
So Ducky Lucky went in and
Foxy Woxy snapped off her head.
Then Goosey Loosey and
Turkey Lurkey went in and
Foxy Woxy snapped off their heads.

Then Cocky Locky went in but
just as Foxy Woxy was going to
snap off his head, he called out
to Henny Penny,
"Run, run, Henny Penny".
So she ran home very fast and
she never did tell the king
that the sky was falling.